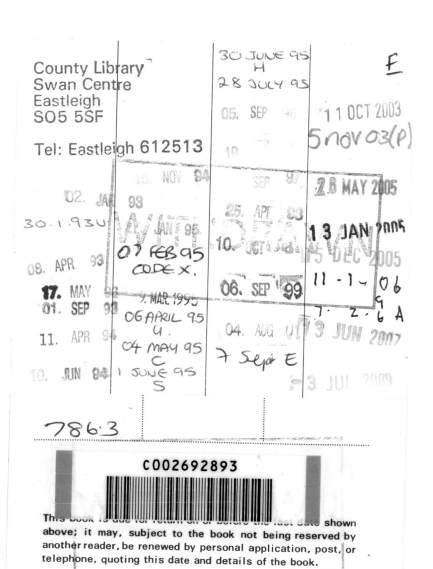
♻ 100% recycled paper.

Alison Bell's

MORE GRADED PIECES FOR PIANO

BOOK 4 : LOWER INTERMEDIATE

Exclusive distributors:
Music Sales Limited, 8/9 Frith Street, London W1V 5TZ. England.
Music Sales Pty Limited, 120 Rothschild Avenue, Rosebery, NSW 2018, Australia.

This book © Copyright 1990: Wise Publications
Order No. AM78833/ISBN 0.7119.2175.X

Art direction by Mike Bell. Book designed by Evelina Frescura
Cover photography by Peter Wood
Typeset by Capital Setters

Music Sales' complete catalogue lists thousands of titles and is free
from your local music shop, or direct from Music Sales Limited. Please send £1 in stamps
for postage to Music Sales Limited, 8/9 Frith Street, London W1V 5TZ.

Printed in the United Kingdom by
J.B. Offset Printers (Marks Tey) Limited, Marks Tey, Essex.

YESTERDAY

WORDS & MUSIC: JOHN LENNON & PAUL McCARTNEY

3

ANN VERONICA

WORDS: DAVID CROFT
MUSIC: CYRIL ORNADEL

BIG SPENDER

WORDS: DOROTHY FIELDS
MUSIC: CY COLEMAN

A TASTE OF HONEY

WORDS: RIC MARLOW
MUSIC: BOBBY SCOTT

DAY BY DAY

WORDS & MUSIC: STEPHEN SCHWARTZ

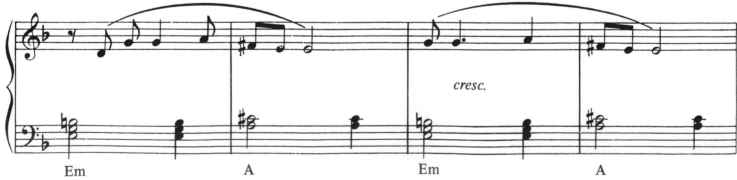

Light Rock Feeling

Em   A   Em

A   Dm   G

Cmaj7   Fmaj7   Cmaj7

Fmaj7   Amaj7

UNDERNEATH THE ARCHES

WORDS & MUSIC: BUD FLANAGAN

THE JEWEL IN THE CROWN
(Theme From)

COMPOSER: GEORGE FENTON

HERNANDO'S HIDEAWAY

WORDS & MUSIC: RICHARD ADLER & JERRY ROSS

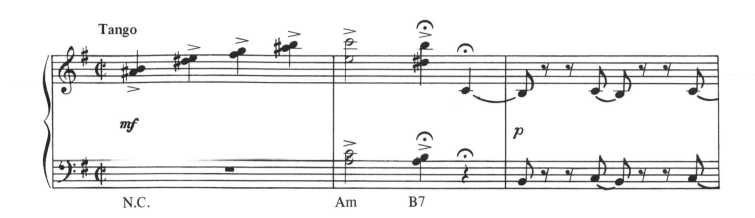

19

BRIDGE OVER TROUBLED WATER

WORDS & MUSIC: PAUL SIMON

ONE

MUSIC: MARVIN HAMLISCH
WORDS: EDWARD KLEBAN

A SPOONFUL OF SUGAR

WORDS & MUSIC: RICHARD M. SHERMAN & ROBERT B. SHERMAN

THE GIRL FROM IPANEMA
(Garota De Ipanema)

ORIGINAL WORDS: VINICIUS DE MORAES
ENGLISH LYRIC: NORMAN GIMBEL
MUSIC: ANTONIO CARLOS JOBIM

BRAZIL

MUSIC: ARY BARROSO
ENGLISH LYRIC: S.K. RUSSELL

UP, UP AND AWAY

WORDS & MUSIC: JIM WEBB

THE INCREDIBLE HULK (Theme From)

COMPOSER: JOE HARNELL